# Specials!

# Scientific investigation, plants, rocks and outer space

Gill Murphy

# Acknowledgements

© 2006 Folens Limited, on behalf of the author.

United Kingdom: Folens Publishers, Apex Business Centre, Boscombe Road, Dunstable, LU5 4RL.
Email: folens@folens.com

Ireland: Folens Publishers, Greenhills Road, Tallaght, Dublin 24.
Email: info@folens.ie

Poland: JUKA, ul. Renesansowa 38, Warsaw 01-905

Editor: Saskia Gwinn                    Layout artist: Book Matrix                    Illustrations: Steph Dix of GCI
Cover design: Holbrook Design           Cover image: Corbis

First published 2006 by Folens Limited.

British Library Cataloguing in Publication Data. A catalogue record for this publication is available from the British Library.

ISBN 1 84303 882 X

# Contents

# Introduction

The Folens **Specials! Science** series meets the requirements for the Key Stage 3 National Curriculum in the United Kingdom, and is compatible with the Schemes of Work published in England by the Qualifications and Curriculum Authority (QCA) and the Scottish 5–14 Guidelines.

The new Key Stage 3 **Specials!** series has been developed in response to extensive research, which identifies how to aid students with lower reading abilities. Its photocopiable format with easy to follow Activity sheets, accompanied by a detailed set of teacher's instructions, will enable students to make the most of their learning experience. All books in the Folens **Specials!** series have been assessed through research carried out within the schooling community.

**Scientific investigation, plants, rocks and outer space** contains the scientific topics required at Key Stage 3, and has been completed for students with a reading age of between six and nine. The book is divided into ten sections, containing photocopiable Activity sheets, which can be used by individual students or as part of a group activity. Practical activities are included in most units, where students are encouraged to work in small groups using writing frames to plan their own experiments. Teachers can make the most of photocopiable Activity sheets, which can be used by individual students or as an excellent aid for group projects.

**Teacher's notes** are provided for the teacher as guidance when using **Activity sheets.** They comprise a set of learning **Objectives,** which detail the skills students will acquire in each individual unit. **Prior knowledge** has been set out, referring to scientific knowledge, which students will already be familiar with, in order that they can complete each unit successfully. **Background** information has also been provided for each unit and gives an overview of the individual topics, highlighting how different pages can be linked together. In addition to the **Activity sheets,** a **Starter activity** has been included to introduce each unit or relate it to a previous topic.

**Activity sheets** are intended to be taught consecutively and contain a variety of tasks, including sequencing work, filling in the gaps, constructing posters, as well as ICT to prepare individual presentations and practical sessions. A suggested **Plenary,** which can be found within the accompanying **Teacher's notes,** can be used to recall key points and important terminology within each section.

An **Assessment sheet,** which can be found at the end of the book, is intended to highlight the student's progress, whereby students can identify successful tasks they have completed during the course of the book. At this stage, students will be able to provide examples of their own work to support their answers. Assessment sheets are a useful tool for teachers to determine the level at which each student is working.

Look out for other titles in the Folens **Specials! Science** series, which include:

- Chemical reactions, materials and particles
- Energy, electricity and movement
- Life processes and the environment

# Teacher's notes

## Solar system and beyond

### Objectives

- Understand that day and night are due to the Earth's rotation
- Know why there are different seasons
- Identify that the Earth is one of nine planets
- Learn more about the conditions on other planets.

### Prior knowledge

Students should know that our planet, the Earth, is one of a number of planets that orbit the Sun.

### QCA link

Unit 7L Solar system and beyond

### NC links

Sc4 Physical processes 4a, 4b, 4d, 4e

### Scottish attainment targets

Environmental studies - Science - Earth and space
Strand - Earth in space
Level E, C

## Background

The Sun is the star at the centre of our Solar System. There are nine planets orbiting our Sun. It takes our Earth one year to orbit the Sun. Those planets closer to the Sun have shorter orbits, while Pluto the furthest away, takes about 248 years to complete one orbit of the Sun.

### Starter activity

Ask students the question, *'Before we had clocks, how did people know what time it was?'*

### Activity sheets

'Earth'. Ask students to fill in the introduction using the word bank provided. Ask them to read instructions one to five, which will enable them to label the diagram that follows overleaf.

'Looking south'. Students should use the instructions provided on page 6 ('Earth') to label the diagram provided and find out more about the Sun's place in context to Earth.

'Day or night'? Show students a globe of the world, with a red X on it to represent the UK. Use a bright bench light (this will represent the Sun) to illustrate how day and night occur. Students should use this information to complete the questions, which follow.

'The seasons'. Use the same globe and bench light to illustrate how the tilt of the Earth gives us different seasons. A diagram has been provided on the activity sheet. Students should use the demonstration to fill in the introductory text and then the boxes. Ask students to make a poster illustrating the different seasons. For example, a snow scene could represent winter.

'What is an eclipse?' explains what happens when a solar eclipse and lunar eclipse occur. Students should study the information on the sheet, filling in the introductory text. A diagram has been provided to show students what happens when a solar eclipse occurs. Ask students to label the diagram using the boxes provided. Encourage students to draw a similar diagram to represent a lunar eclipse.

'Solar system'. Instruct students to complete the introductory text, using the word bank provided. Divide the class into groups and give each group a picture of each of the nine planets. Ask students to work together to put the planets in order, starting nearest the Sun. Using the example provided as a guide, ask students to work within their groups, to create a new sentence for remembering the order of the planets.

'Planets'. Students can learn more about the planets by constructing their own planet spinner, using the template provided. Teachers should make an enlarged copy and stick it onto A3 card for students to make their spinner. Ask students to use ICT to find out two interesting facts about each planet. They should then write down what they have learnt in the relevant section of their spinner. Leave five minutes before the end of the lesson for each student to tell the rest of the group their interesting fact.

### Plenary

Ask students to identify where all the stars, which we can see at night, go to during the day.

# Earth

☞ Complete the text below, using the word bank provided.

The Earth has an imaginary line called the a _ _ _ that passes through the North and
S _ _ _ _ poles. The Earth s _ _ _ _ on its axis and at the same time it is moving around
the S _ _ . The half of the Earth that is facing the Sun is in d _ _ _ _ _ _ _ and the half
facing away from the Sun is in n _ _ _ _ .

It takes one d _ _ for the Earth to spin once on its axis. We divide that day into twenty
four h _ _ _ _ . The time taken for the Earth to complete one o _ _ _ _ of the Sun is
called a y _ _ _ . This is just over 365 d _ _ _ .

**Word bank**

daylight   hours   South   Sun   year   axis
days   orbit   day   spins   night

As the Earth spins it makes the Sun appear to move across the sky. This spinning also
makes the stars appear to move across the sky. The Sun and stars do not really move.

☞ Study the diagram provided in 'Looking south' over the page. Now, on the diagram,
carry out the following tasks.

1. Draw the Sun in the sky at midday in the summer. Label this drawing with an **S**.

2. Draw an arc to show how the Sun appears to move across the sky during the day.

3. Put arrows on your line to show the direction in which the Sun is moving.

4. Now, draw the Sun in the sky at midday during the winter. Label this drawing
with a **W**.

5. Which season has the longest days, summer or winter?

**Specials!**

## Looking south

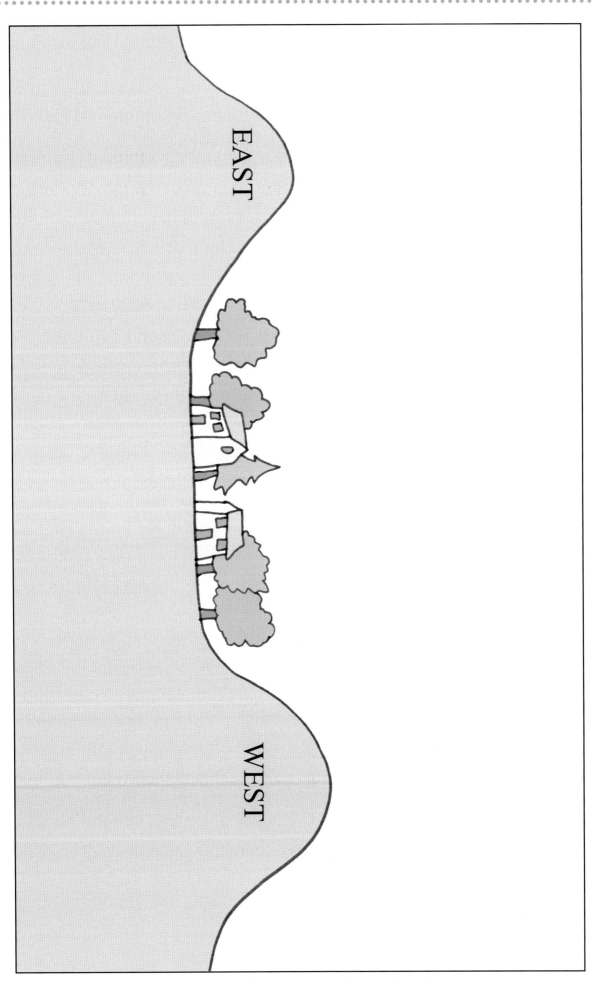

EAST

WEST

# Day or night?

Below are some drawings showing the Earth spinning around on its axis. The big X on the diagrams shows the position of the town where Peter lives. Each arrow next to the Earth shows the direction in which the Earth is spinning.

☞ Your teacher will illustrate to you how day and night occur. Use the demonstration and the drawings to answer the questions, which follow. Then, in your work books, draw a picture of Peter's view of the Sun in the sky at each time of day.

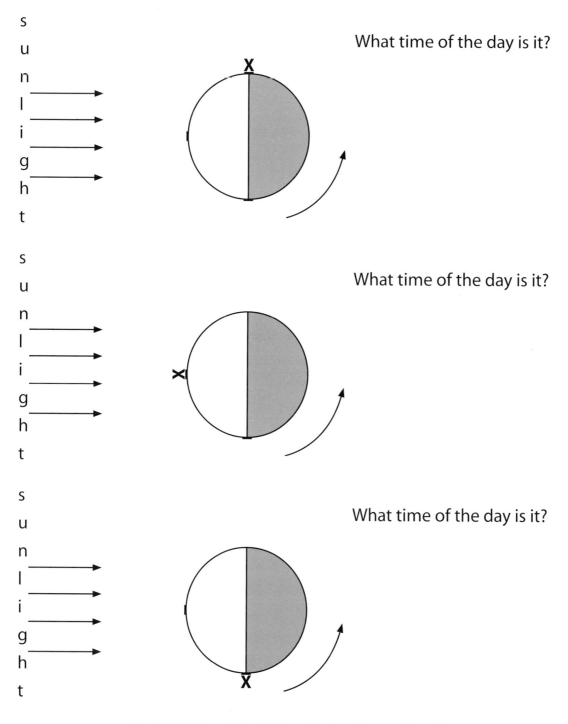

What time of the day is it?

What time of the day is it?

What time of the day is it?

**Specials!** Science Scientific investigation, plants, rocks and outer space    © Folens (copiable page)

# The seasons

☞ Complete the text about seasons below. Use a word bank provided by your teacher to help you.

**Here in the United Kingdom we have four seasons each year.**

Summer is w _ _ _ with l _ _ _ days and s _ _ _ _ nights.

Winter is c _ _ _ with s _ _ _ _ days and l _ _ _ nights.

Spring comes between winter and s _ _ _ _ _ and autumn comes after summer and b _ _ _ _ _ _ winter.

☞ Now, study the diagram below. This diagram shows us how the tilt of the Earth gives us different seasons. Complete each box below. Then, copy the diagram into your work books and use the completed boxes to label it.

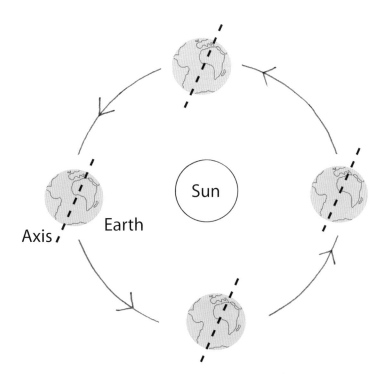

✂ ------------------------
Northern hemisphere = summer
Southern hemisphere = w _ _ _ _ _

✂ ------------------------
Northern hemisphere = spring
Southern hemisphere = a _ _ _ _ _

✂ ------------------------
Northern hemisphere = w _ _ _ _ _
Southern hemisphere = s _ _ _ _ _

✂ ------------------------
Northern hemisphere = autumn
Southern hemisphere = s _ _ _ _ _

# What is an eclipse?

☞ What is a solar eclipse? Complete the text below.

A solar eclipse happens when the Sun, the M _ _ _ and the E _ _ _ _ are all lined up.
The Moon is in the m_ _ _ _ _ .

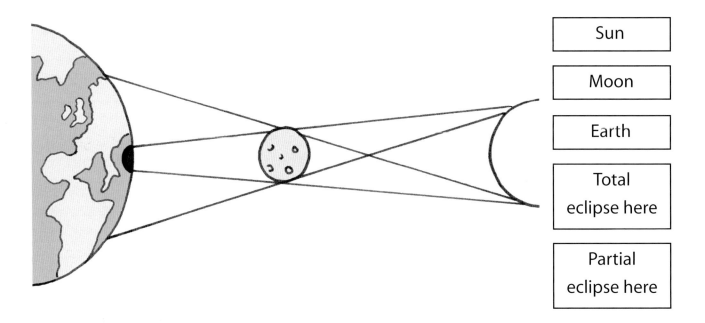

| Sun |
|---|
| Moon |
| Earth |
| Total eclipse here |
| Partial eclipse here |

☞ Connect the boxes above to their correct place on the diagram of a solar eclipse to label the different parts.

**A solar eclipse** does not block out the Sun all over the Earth. The last solar eclipse in the UK was 1999 and we will have to wait until 2090 for the next one!

**A lunar eclipse** happens when the Earth is lined up between the Moon and the Sun, so that the Earth blocks out the Sun's light from the Moon. This is also quite rare. A lunar eclipse can last as long as two hours because the Earth's shadow is much bigger than the Moon's shadow.

☞ In your work books, draw a diagram (similar to the one above) to show a lunar eclipse. Use the same boxes as before to label the diagram.

# Solar system

☞ Complete the sentences below, using the word bank provided.

**Word bank**

orbit    light    quickest    heat    Sun    large    light
see    centre    lowest    Nine    reflected

- The Sun is a source of
  l _ _ _ _ and h _ _ _ .

- The Sun is huge and has a l _ _ _ _ gravitational pull on the planets. This keeps them in o _ _ _ _ .

- The S _ _ is at the c _ _ _ _ _ of our solar system. N _ _ _ planets orbit the Sun.

- Planets do not give off l _ _ _ _ . We can only s _ _ the planets because light from the Sun is r _ _ _ _ _ _ _ _ off them.

- The planets move around the Sun in an elliptical shaped orbit (shaped like a squashed circle).

- The planets nearest the Sun move the q _ _ _ _ _ _ _ because they feel the l _ _ _ _ _ force.

☞ Below you will find a list of planets which appear in their correct order from the Sun. Next to it is a sentence which will help you to remember the planets in this order. Make up your own sentence to help you to remember the order of the planets.

| Planets in order from the Sun | | |
| --- | --- | --- |
| Mercury | My | M _____ |
| Venus | Very | V _____ |
| Earth | Easy | E _____ |
| Mars | Method | M _____ |
| Jupiter | Just | J _____ |
| Saturn | Speeds | S _____ |
| Uranus | Up | U _____ |
| Neptune | Naming | N _____ |
| Pluto | Planets | P _____ |

# Activity sheet – Solar system and beyond

# Planets

☞ The two circles below can be used to make a spinner to help you learn about the different planets. Cut out the circles and follow the instructions provided to make your spinner.

1.   Your teacher will provide you with a large copy of the two circles below. Cut out the first circle (A) carefully. In each section, draw a picture of the named planet. Use text books to find out the time it takes for each planet to orbit the sun.

**Circle A**

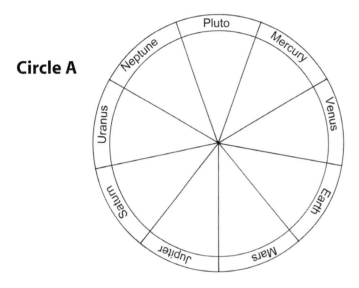

2.   Cut out this circle (B) and the shaded area.

**Circle B**

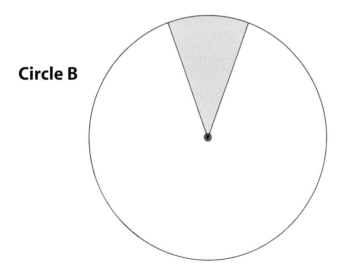

3.   Put circle B on top of circle A and hold in place with a split pin.

☞ Now, use ICT to find out two interesting facts about each planet. Tell the rest of the class what you have found out.

# Teacher's notes

## Gravity and space

### Objectives

- Know that gravity is a force
- Understand that the pull of the Sun's gravity holds the planets in their orbits
- Know that the Moon is a natural satellite of the Earth
- Understand how we use the artificial satellites, which orbit the Earth

### Prior knowledge

Students will know that the Sun and the planets which orbit it, form our Solar system (Solar system and beyond 7L). Students should also know that the Earth has a gravitational force. Students should use their knowledge of the units for weight and mass. (Forces and their effects 7K) for this topic.

### QCA link

Gravity and space 9J

### NC links

Sc4 Physical processes 2b, 4c, 4e

### Scottish attainment targets

Environmental studies - Science - Earth and space
Strand - Earth in space
Level D

## Background

Gravity is a force, which acts between two masses, pulling them together. It is the force of the Earth's gravity that keeps the Moon and other satellites in orbit. The Sun has a huge mass. It is the attraction between the Sun and the planets, which keeps the planets orbiting round the Sun.

### Starter activity

Ask students to write down the names of the planets in order, starting nearest the Sun.

### Activity sheets

'What can you remember about the Solar system?' will remind students what they have learnt about the Solar system in order to prepare them for the activities, which follow. Students should answer all the questions before moving onto the next activity sheet.

'What is Gravity?' Ask students to complete the introductory text. Encourage students to work as a class, to complete the activity about how to calculate mass and weight, which follows. A diagram has been provided to show students how the pull of the Earth's gravity changes. Ask students to study the diagram and answer the questions, which follow.

'Gravity and distance'. Ask students to complete the introductory text, and then study the diagram which follows. Students should explain what is happening to the space ship in the diagram by filling in the text. A word bank has been provided to help them.

'Solar system models'. Encourage students to use ICT to find out more about the ideas of Copernicus and Galileo. Once they have completed the introductory text, tell students to label the diagram of the solar system. You may need to provide students with a word bank to help them complete the introductory text.

'Man-made satellites' includes an information sheet, which explains to students how we use satellites. Ask students to use the information to create a spider diagram to break down what they have learnt. Once they have completed this, ask students to work in small groups, using ICT and the Internet to find out more about space crafts and the Global Positioning System (GPS).

### Plenary

Ask one or two of each of the groups to present their findings to the class.

# What can you remember about the solar system?

☞ Answer the questions below. Use what you have already learnt about the solar system to help you.

1. Why does the Sun look brighter than the other stars?

   _____

2. How many hours does it take for the Earth to spin around once?

   _____

3. Why do the stars appear to move slowly westward at night?

   _____

4. Try to explain why we have day and night.

   _____

5. We can see lots of stars at night but where do all the stars go during the day?

   _____

6. How long does it take for the Earth to travel once round the Sun?

   _____

7. How many times does the Earth spin on its axis while it makes this journey?

   _____

8. Name all the planets in the correct order, starting nearest the Sun.

   _____

9. Which is the biggest planet?

   _____

10. Which is the coldest planet?

   _____

# What is gravity? Sheet 1

☞ Gravity is a pulling force. Complete the text below, using a word bank provided by your teacher.

When you kick a ball up into the a _ _ it falls back down t _ _ _ _ _ _ the ground and towards the

c _ _ _ _ _ of the Earth. It does not matter if you are in Australia or E _ _ _ _ _ _ , the ball will still fall d _ _ _ towards the centre of the Earth. Gravity is the f _ _ _ _ that holds us down on the surface of the Earth and s _ _ _ _ us floating away into s _ _ _ _ .

☞ Study the information below. Gravity is not the same on every planet or even on the Moon. The larger planets have a bigger gravitational pull.

---

**Mass is a measure of how much material there is in something.**

**Mass is measured in kilograms (kg).**

**Weight is what we call the pull of gravity on a mass.**

**Weight is measured in Newtons (N).**

---

Captain Azid has a mass of 70kg. Wherever he goes in space and whichever planet he lands on, his mass will stay the same.

We know the force of gravity on Earth is 10N/kg
We can find out Captain Azid's weight on Earth like this:

Weight  in N = mass in kg      x gravity in N/kg
              =  70 kg         x 10 N/kg
              = 7000 N

**Captain Azid**

☞ Now, turn over to the next page to find out how Captain Azid's weight changes.

# What is gravity? Sheet 2

☞ Complete this table to find out how Captain Azid's weight and mass changes on his travels.

| Where he landed | His mass (kg) | Gravity (N/kg) | His weight (N) |
|---|---|---|---|
| Moon | | 1.6 | |
| Mercury | | 4 | |
| Jupiter | | 26 | |
| Saturn | | 11 | |
| Pluto | | 20 | |

We already know that a planet with a large mass, like Earth, has a stronger gravitational field than a much smaller mass like the Moon.

☞ Study the diagram below to see how the pull of the Earth's gravity changes as you move further away from the planet.

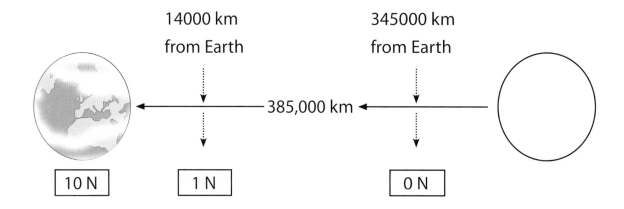

☞ Now, complete the following tasks.

1. On the diagram, label the Earth and the Moon.

2. What do you think the effect of the Earth's gravity will be half way between the Earth and the Moon? _____ N

3. When would an astronaut feel weightless?

_____

**Specials!** Science Scientific investigation, plants, rocks and outer space     © Folens (copiable page)

# Gravity and distance

Remember what you learnt in 'What is gravity?' to help you to complete this activity sheet.

☞ How do spaceships leave the Earth? To overcome the Earth's gravitational field, a spaceship needs:

A thrust (l_ _ _ _ _ _ force) b_ _ _ _ _ than its weight.

☞ Study the diagram below and complete the text which follows, using the word bank provided.

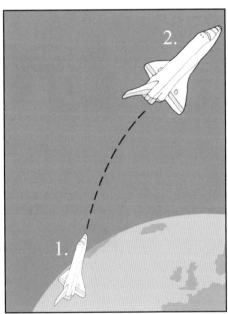

1. The space ship l _ _ _ _ off when the t _ _ _ _ _ from the engines is b _ _ _ _ _ _ than its weight. A spaceship is full of f _ _ _ . As the fuel burns, the mass of the spaceship gets l _ _ _ so it needs less thrust.

2. Further away from the E _ _ _ _ _ the p _ _ _ of gravity is less and the weight of the spaceship also gets l _ _ _ .

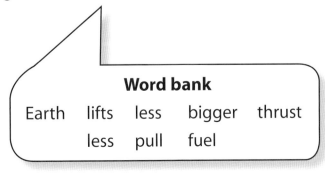

**Word bank**

Earth   lifts   less   bigger   thrust

less   pull   fuel

# Solar system models

☞ Using what you have already learnt about gravity and space, complete the text below. Your teacher will provide you with a word bank to help you.

● Our Sun is only a medium sized s _ _ _ . It looks much b _ _ _ _ _ and much brighter than the other stars because it is so c _ _ _ _ to us.

● Our planet Earth is one of n _ _ _ planets that orbit the Sun. The Sun and all its nine orbiting p _ _ _ _ _ _ make up our s _ _ _ _ s _ _ _ _ _ .

● There are also some c _ _ _ _ _ and asteroids in our solar system. In the past, people believed that the Earth was the centre of the Universe. They thought that the Sun moved around the Earth.

The picture below is a model of the Solar system, which we use today. It is based on the work of Sir Isaac Newton and shows that the path of the planets' orbits around the Sun is elliptical (oval) and not circular.

☞ On the diagram label each **planet** and the **Asteroid belt.**

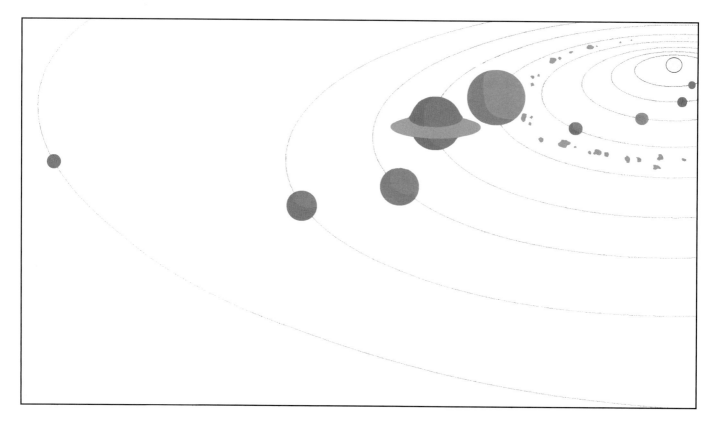

# Activity sheet – Gravity and space

# Man-made satellites sheet 1

☞ Study the information on this sheet. Make a spider diagram, to explain how we use satellites. This information will help you to complete the activity on the next page.

### Satellites

An object which orbits round the Earth is called a satellite. The Moon orbits the Earth and is a natural satellite. There are lots of man-made satellites orbiting the Earth. They are used to communicate between different places, monitor the weather and observe outer space.

### Communication satellites

Communication satellites orbit the Earth about 36000km above the equator. At this height it takes each satellite exactly one day to orbit the Earth. This is called a geostationary orbit because the satellite appears to stay in one place. Telephone signals are sent all over the world using these communication satellites. There is only room in space for 400 communication satellites, any more and they would interfere with each other's signals. You could use books or the Internet to find out how satellite TV works.

### Weather satellites

Weather satellites orbit much closer to the Earth and take about 90 minutes for each complete orbit. As they orbit, the Earth spins below them. These satellites see different parts of the Earth and are used to help forecast the weather.

### Observing the stars

Astronomers have difficulty looking at the stars from the Earth so they put telescopes on satellites, which orbit above the Earth's atmosphere.

# Man-made satellites sheet 2

☞ Study the picture below. Draw lines from each label below to its correct place on the picture.

| Clouds can block out the stars. | Factories pollute the air with dirt particles. | Bright lights from cities make it difficult to see the stars. |

☞ Use the Internet and ICT to find out about the following:

- The Hubble Space telescope.
- GPS (Global Positioning System), what does it do and how does it work?

# Teacher's notes

## Rocks and weathering

### Objectives

- Know what a rock is
- Understand how rocks are broken down by different types of weathering
- Be able to design and carry out own experiment

### Prior knowledge

Students should know the chemical test used to identify carbon dioxide gas (Simple chemical reactions 7F). Students should be able to select suitable equipment for use in an experiment. Students should also know how to interpret the results of their own experiment. (Investigating scientific questions 9M).

### QCA link

*Unit 8G* Rocks and weathering

### NC links

*Sc3* Materials and their properties 1g, 2d, 2e, 2f

### Scottish attainment targets

Environmental studies - Science - Earth and space
Strand - Materials from Earth
Level D

## Background

The process by which rocks are broken down to make soil is called weathering. Weathering has a chemical, physical or biological cause. Chemical weathering due to acid rain can lead to the formation of caves. The continual weathering of rocks can cause erosion of the coastline and silting up of estuaries.

### Starter activity

Ask students to write down five things they know about rocks. Use this information to create a spider diagram.

### Activity sheets

'What are rocks made of?' Tell students to complete the word gaps about rocks, using the word bank provided. Ask students to form small groups. Instruct students to look at rock samples using a hand lens. Students should then draw pictures of what they can see in the boxes provided.

'Weathering of rocks' looks at three different types of weathering. Read through the activity sheet with the whole class, creating a word bank on the board as you fill in the missing text. Ask students to then create a colourful poster to illustrate the different ways in which rocks are broken down.

'Weathering and temperature'. Ask students to divide a clean sheet of A4 paper into two columns. At the top of one column, students should write, 'Freeze and thaw' and at the top of the other, 'Heating and cooling'. Students should then cut out the boxes provided and place them in the correct order in the correct column.

'Weathering'. Ask students, in pairs, to use the writing frames provided, to design their own experiment to find out the effect of acid rain on limestone. Instruct students to then work with their partner to carry out the experiment. Writing frames have also been provided for the students' results and evaluation. Encourage students to use their results to complete the final activity about limestone.

### Plenary

Show students a sample of rainwater and ask how they would find out how acidic it was.

# What are rocks made of?

☞ Complete these sentences about rocks, using the word bank provided.

> **Word bank**
>
> bubbles    materials    solid    sand    grains    water    grains    minerals
>
> ground        geologists        rock    material    formula    porous

1. **What is a rock?**

    A rock is a s _ _ _ _ non living m _ _ _ _ _ _ _ found in the g _ _ _ _ _ . Scientists called g _ _ _ _ _ _ _ _ _ study rocks. Geologists even call s _ _ _ a rock.

2. **What are rocks made of?**

    Rocks are made of substances called m _ _ _ _ _ _ _ . Each mineral has its own chemical f _ _ _ _ _ _ . The m _ _ _ _ _ _ _ _ in the rocks are in little bits called g _ _ _ _ _ .

3. **Porous and non-porous rocks.**

    If a r _ _ _ has spaces between the g _ _ _ _ _ we say it is p _ _ _ _ _ . We can tell if a rock is porous by putting w _ _ _ _ on it. If b _ _ _ _ _ _ appear, it means that the rock is porous.

☞ Use a hand lens to look at some porous and non-porous rock samples. Draw a picture of each rock type in the space provided below.

| Non-porous | Porous |
|---|---|
|  |  |

# Weathering of rocks

**Chemical weathering**

When acid rain falls onto rocks, there is a reaction and a new substance is made.

**Physical weathering**

No new substance is made during physical weathering. The rocks are broken into smaller pieces.

**Biological weathering**

This happens when living things cause the rocks to break apart or wear away.

☞ Complete the text about weathering of rocks. Your teacher will provide you with a word bank to help you.

Roots of p _ _ _ _ _ grow into small cracks in rocks pushing them a _ _ _ _ and making the cracks b _ _ _ _ _ . The bigger the plant g _ _ _ _ the bigger the c _ _ _ _ in the rock will become.

This is called b _ _ _ _ _ _ _ _ _ weathering.

Waves pounding onto r _ _ _ _ gradually make them s _ _ _ _ _ _ .

This is called p _ _ _ _ _ _ _ weathering.

Old grave stones are difficult to r _ _ _ because acid rain has gradually w _ _ _ away the lettering.

This is called c _ _ _ _ _ _ _ weathering.

☞ Now, in groups, create a poster to show the different ways that rocks are broken down.

# Weathering and temperature

☞ Divide a clean A4 sheet of plain paper into two columns. Label one column **Freeze and thaw**. Label the other column **Heating and cooling**. Now, cut out the boxes below and put them in the correct order to describe how rocks can be weathered by freeze and thaw and heating and cooling. Stick each description in its correct column. Check with your teacher before you stick them in.

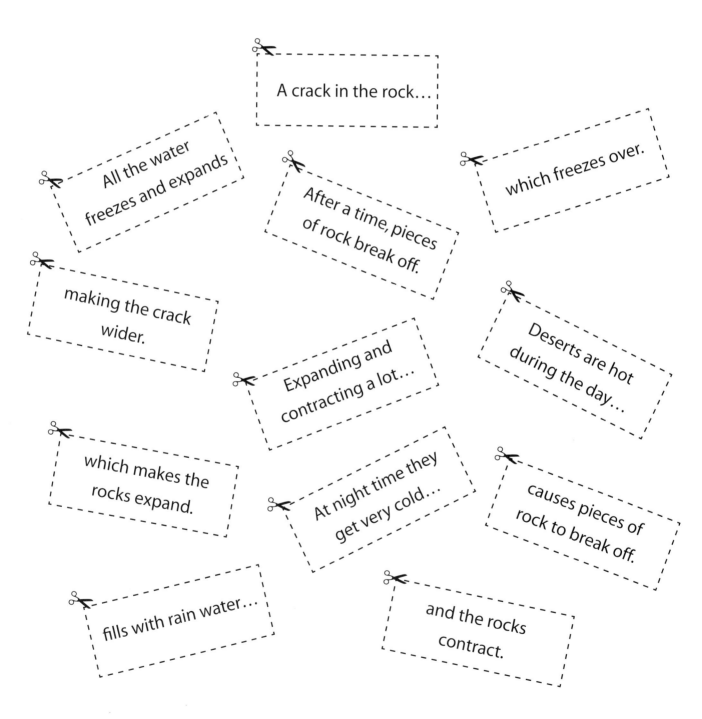

A crack in the rock…

All the water freezes and expands

After a time, pieces of rock break off.

which freezes over.

making the crack wider.

Deserts are hot during the day…

Expanding and contracting a lot…

which makes the rocks expand.

At night time they get very cold…

causes pieces of rock to break off.

fills with rain water…

and the rocks contract.

# Weathering sheet 1

☞ Study the information below.

Limestone is a white rock. It was made thousands of years ago from dead sea creatures.

When rain falls through air polluted with sulphur dioxide gas, it combines with the gas to make a weak acid. We call it **acid rain.**

☞ Now, in pairs, design an experiment to show what happens to limestone when acid rain falls onto it. Use the writing frames provided below to help you. Once you have planned your experiment, carry it out to see what happens. Check your experiment with your teacher first.

**What equipment will you need?**
Draw and label a diagram of your equipment here.

**Method**
Describe exactly what you would do.

_____

_____

_____

# Weathering sheet 2

---

**Results**

What would you expect to see happening?

_____

_____

_____

---

**Evaluation**

Using your knowledge of chemistry, try to explain your results.

_____

_____

_____

---

**Limestone** has the chemical name calcium carbonate.

☞ During your experiment, you may have noticed that a gas was produced. Do you know what this gas is?

☞ What test could you use to confirm your answer in the question above?

☞ In your work books, draw and label a diagram to explain the test you have chosen.

## The rock cycle

### Objectives

- Know the names of the three main types of rocks and be able to give examples
- Identify how each type of rock is formed
- Understand what happens in the rock cycle

### Prior knowledge

Students should know how rocks are broken down by weathering (Rocks and weathering 8G).

### QCA link

*Unit 8H* The rock cycle

### NC links

*Sc3* Materials and their properties 1a, 1b, 2e, 2f

### Scottish attainment targets

Environmental studies - Science - Earth and space
Strand - Materials from Earth
Level D

## Background

There are three main types of rocks: igneous, sedimentary and metamorphic. The rock cycle is a continuous and ongoing process. Igneous rocks are formed from volcanic action. Through weathering and erosion, they are deposited as layers which eventually become sedimentary rocks. Increases in temperature and pressure, change sedimentary rocks into metamorphic rocks.

### Starter activity

Show students a short video of an erupting volcano.

### Activity sheets

'How are sedimentary rocks made? sheets 1 and 2.' Sheet 1 is a sequencing activity. Ask students to cut out the word boxes provided and arrange them in their correct order to create a flow chart to explain how sedimentary rocks are formed. Students should then use their completed flow chart to label the cross section diagram provided on the second sheet, which will need to be enlarged to A3.

'Rock types' looks at the three main types of rocks. Ask students to fill in the chart about all three, using the word bank provided. A diagram follows. Tell students to make a large copy of the diagram in their work books, and label the oldest and the youngest layers of rock.

'The rock cycle' is a resource sheet, which provides students with a diagram representing the rock cycle. Labels, which complete the diagram are provided on its accompanying activity sheet. Tell students to cut out the labels and stick them in the correct place on the diagram. This will enable them to mark examples of the different rock types on their diagram using what they have learnt.

### Plenary

Show students different named examples of rocks to identify as sedimentary, metamorphic or igneous.

# How are sedimentary rocks made? Sheet 1

☞ Cut out the boxes below. Put them in their correct order to make a flow chart. This flow chart will explain how sedimentary rocks are formed.

| Pieces of rock are broken off the mountain by weathering. |

⬇

| We call the sand and pebbles that settle on the seabed 'sediment'. |

⬇

| After millions of years these layers of sediment have been squashed so much that they have formed 'sedimentary rocks'. |

⬇

| As the rocks are carried down the river they rub against each other, getting smaller and smoother to make pebbles and sand. |

⬇

| Rivers carry the pieces of rock down to the sea. |

⬇

| The layers of sediment get squashed and pressed down as more and more layers of sediment form on top. |

⬇

| These pieces get into streams and rivers. |

⬇

| When the river gets near the sea it slows down and drops the pebbles and sand on the seabed. |

# Activity sheet – The rock cycle

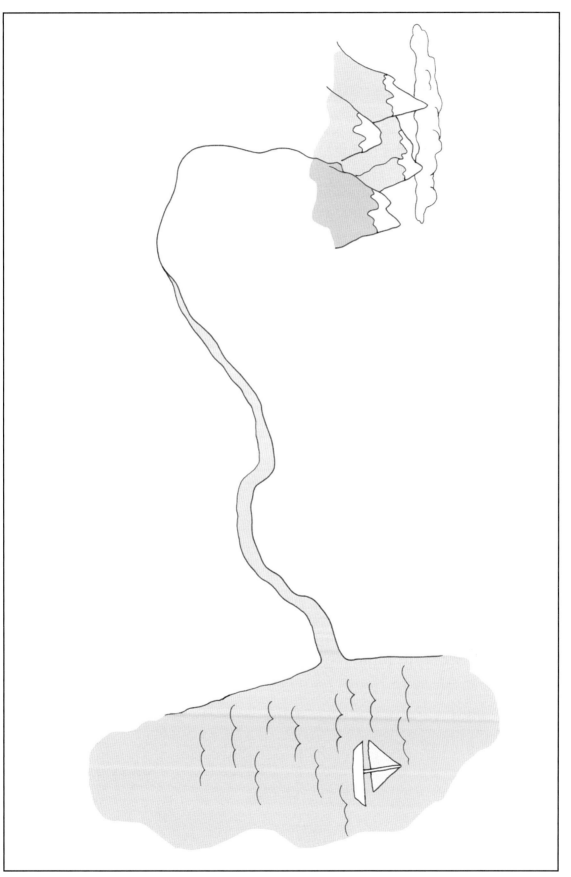

## How are sedimentary rocks made? Sheet 2

☞ Now copy the sentences from your flow chart into the correct position on this diagram, to show how sedimentary rocks are formed. Your teacher will give you a large copy.

# Rock types

☞ Complete the chart below using the word bank.

**Word bank**

fossils    heated    sand    quickly    millions    rocks
slowly    shells    small    sediment    large

| Rock type | How was it made? | Examples |
|---|---|---|
| Igneous | Are made from other r _ _ _ _ that have melted.<br>They have small crystals if cool q _ _ _ _ _ _ and large crystals if cool s _ _ _ _ _ . | ● Granite has l _ _ _ _ crystals.<br>● Basalt has s _ _ _ _ crystals. |
| Metamorphic | Are made when other rocks are h _ _ _ _ _ under pressure and have small crystals arranged in bands or layers. | ● Slate made from mudstone.<br>● Marble made from limestone. |
| Sedimentary | Are made from layers of s _ _ _ _ _ _ _ .<br>They can take m _ _ _ _ _ _ _ of years to form and can sometimes contain f _ _ _ _ _ _ . | ● Sandstone, compacted grains of s _ _ _ .<br>● Limestone made from the s _ _ _ _ _ of dead sea creatures. |

☞ In your work books, make a large copy of the diagram provided opposite. On your diagram, label the youngest and oldest layers of rock. Now, identify where you might find the oldest fossils.

chalk

sandstone

limestone

granite

# The rock cycle sheet 1

Rocks can change into other rocks. The stuff that rocks are made from stays the same, but the rocks do not. Over time, one type of rock can be changed into a new type of rock. We call this pattern of changes the **rock cycle**.

☞ Study the diagram below. Then, turn to the next page.

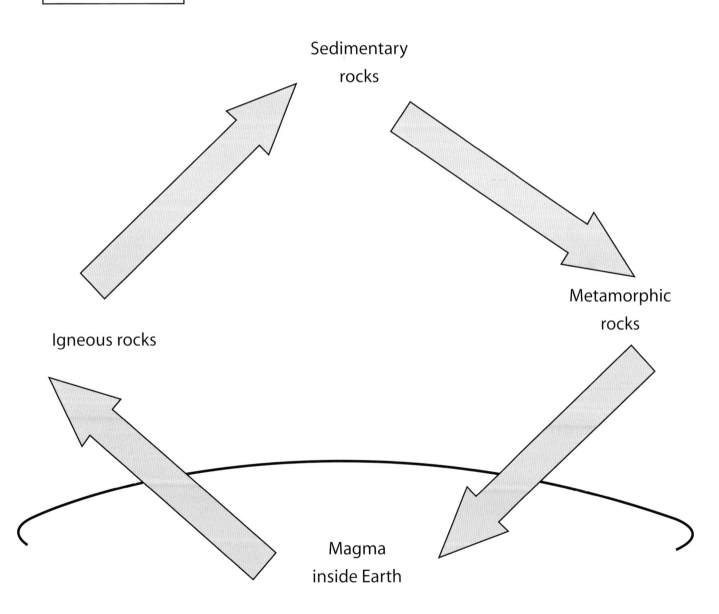

# The rock cycle sheet 2

☞ Now, cut out the statements below and put them in the correct place on your rock cycle diagram on page 31.

You might want to use colours to make your diagram clearer and easier to understand.

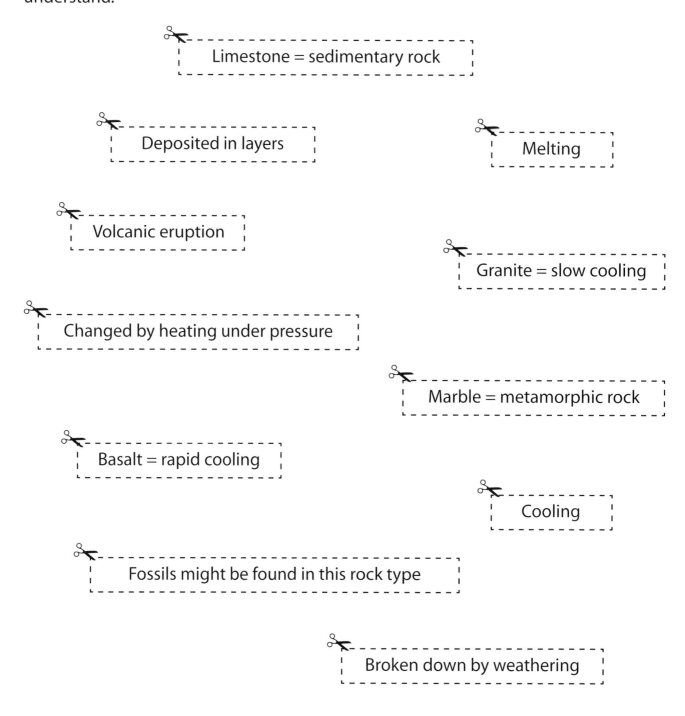

Limestone = sedimentary rock

Deposited in layers

Melting

Volcanic eruption

Granite = slow cooling

Changed by heating under pressure

Marble = metamorphic rock

Basalt = rapid cooling

Cooling

Fossils might be found in this rock type

Broken down by weathering

## Plants and photosynthesis

### Objectives

- Know that plants make their own food using energy from sunlight
- Understand that photosynthesis takes place in the chloroplasts
- Be able to test a leaf for starch
- Identify where water moves around the plant

### Prior knowledge

Students should know the different parts of the plant and the function of each part. Students will understand that green plants make their own food using energy from the Sun and that this process is called photosynthesis (Environment and feeding relationships 7C). Students will already have used iodine to test for starch in different foods (Food and digestion 8A).

### QCA link

Unit 9C Plants and photosynthesis

### NC links

Sc2 Life processes and living things 2k, 3a, 3b, 3c, 3d, 4a, 5a, 5c

### Scottish attainment targets

Environmental studies - Science - living things and the processes of life
Strand - The processes of life
Level E, C

## Background

All living things require food to give them the energy they need to grow and thrive. Green plants synthesise their food using light energy from the Sun. Some plant cells have chloroplasts, which contain the green pigment chlorophyll. Chlorophyll is a green chemical that can trap the energy from sunlight. Photosynthesis can only occur in the green parts of a plant.

### Starter activity

Ask students to draw a simple diagram of a plant and label the different parts of the plant. Tell students to describe the job of each part.

### Activity sheets

'How plants make food'. Ask students to label the different stages of photosynthesis using the word bank provided. Once the text has been completed, encourage students to use what they have learnt to write a word equation for photosynthesis.

'Inside a leaf' provides students with a cross-section diagram of a leaf. Labels for the diagram have been provided. Instruct students to complete the labels. Provide students with a word bank to help them. Students should then use the arrows to join each label to the part of the leaf it relates to. Now, ask students to look at either microscope or bioviewer slides which show a cross section of a leaf. Using what they have learnt, ask students to identify the different parts of the leaf on the slide.

'Testing for starch'. Instruct students to cut out the statements provided. Ask them to arrange the boxes in the correct order to test for starch in a leaf. Once they have done so, they should carry out the experiment.

'When do plants make oxygen?' provides students with an experiment, which shows them how they could see oxygen being made at different times of the day. Results have already been provided for the student. Instruct them to study the results and answer the questions, which follow.

'Moving water around' is a practical activity sheet. Tell students to read through the activity sheet carefully and work in pairs to carry out the experiment. Ask students to draw a series of pictures of the celery stalk after every cut is taken at 5cm intervals. Students should then use their results to answer the final question.

### Plenary

Give students ready-made cards which show each step in the reaction for photosynthesis. Provide students with additional cards for the plus and equals sign. Students should then use the cards to put together an equation to show what happens during photosynthesis.

# How plants make food

☞ The diagram below shows you how plants make their food. This process is called photosynthesis. Complete the diagram to learn about the different stages of photosynthesis. Use the word bank provided to help you.

**Word bank**

leaves    air    Green    roots    Energy    Carbon dioxide

Water    chlorophyll    photosynthesis    glucose    food

Plants make their own f _ _ _ . To do this they need these things:

E _ _ _ _ _ from sunlight.

C _ _ _ _ _ _ d _ _ _ _ _ _ gas from the air.

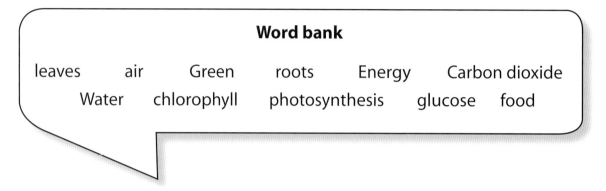

G _ _ _ _ pigment called chlorophyll.

W _ _ _ _ from the soil.

Plants make their food in their green l _ _ _ _ _ . The leaf contains a special green pigment called c _ _ _ _ _ _ _ _ _ _ _ . The food that plants make is called glucose. Plants change the g _ _ _ _ _ _ to starch and store it in the leaves until they need to use it. Water from the soil enters the plant through the r _ _ _ _ .

Carbon dioxide gas from the a _ _ enters the plant through small holes (called stomata) in the leaves. The process in which plants make food is called

p _ _ _ _ _ _ _ _ _ _ _ _ _ .

# Inside a leaf

☞ Fill in the text below to help you label the different parts of a leaf. Use arrows to
mark which part of the leaf each label belongs to.

**Lower epidermis**

Has small holes called s _ _ _ _ _ _ .
Air moves in and out through the
stomata.

**Upper epidermis (skin)**

Clear to let s _ _ _ _ _ _ _
pass through.

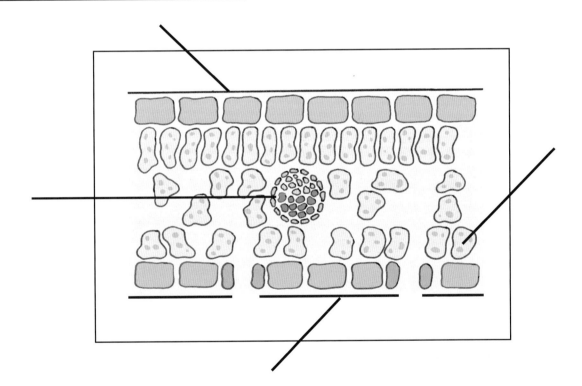

**Spongy layer**

Contains lots of air spaces. Carbon
dioxide gas enters cells here and
o _ _ _ _ _ gas leaves cells.

**Palisade layer**

Long thin cells containing lots of
c _ _ _ _ _ _ _ _ _ _ . This is where
p _ _ _ _ _ _ _ _ _ _ _ _ _ happens.

# Testing for starch

☞ John and Nabil are studying a plant. The plant has green and white striped leaves. They decide to test their plant to see if only the green part of the leaf can make starch.

Their experiment is described in the boxes below, but each step has been muddled up. Cut out each box and put it in the correct order to show John and Nabil's experiment. When they are in the correct order, stick them in your work books.

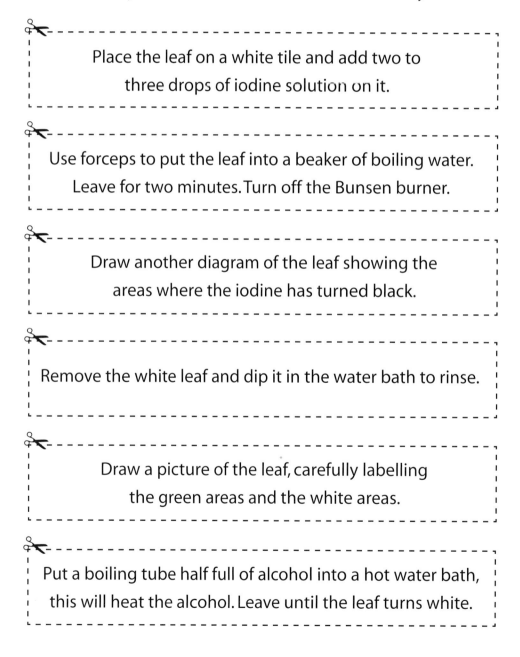

Place the leaf on a white tile and add two to three drops of iodine solution on it.

Use forceps to put the leaf into a beaker of boiling water. Leave for two minutes. Turn off the Bunsen burner.

Draw another diagram of the leaf showing the areas where the iodine has turned black.

Remove the white leaf and dip it in the water bath to rinse.

Draw a picture of the leaf, carefully labelling the green areas and the white areas.

Put a boiling tube half full of alcohol into a hot water bath, this will heat the alcohol. Leave until the leaf turns white.

☞ Now, carry out the experiment to test for starch, using the boxes to guide you.

# When do plants make oxygen?

☞ Next, John and Nabil want to find out when the plant makes the most oxygen. They decide to use a plant that grows in water to see the bubbles. The experiment they used is drawn below.

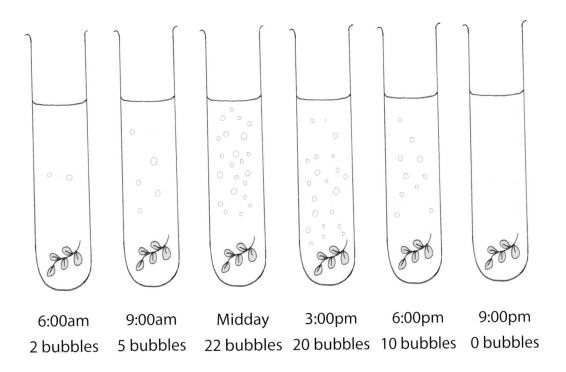

| 6:00am | 9:00am | Midday | 3:00pm | 6:00pm | 9:00pm |
| 2 bubbles | 5 bubbles | 22 bubbles | 20 bubbles | 10 bubbles | 0 bubbles |

☞ Use John and Nabil's results above to draw a bar chart on squared paper, showing the number of bubbles produced by the pondweed at different times of the day. Then, answer these questions.

1.   When did the pond weed make the most bubbles?

2.   When did the pond weed stop making bubbles?

3.   What do you think affected the rate at which the pond weed made oxygen?

# Moving water around

☞ A new class want to look at how water moves around a plant. Below are some of their thoughts. Find out if they are right by completing the experiment, which follows. You should work in pairs.

Water enters the plant through the roots. How does it get to the leaves?

I think it moves up through the stem.

You're right, but how can we see the water moving?

1. Cut the bottom of the celery stalk and put it into a beaker of water.

2. Add three to four drops of red food colour to the water.

3. Leave for ten minutes.

4. After ten minutes, cut across the celery stalk (about 5cm from the bottom). Draw what you can see opposite.

5. Continue cutting the celery stalk every 5cm until you reach the leaves.

☞ What has this experiment shown you about the movement of water in the celery stalk?

# Teacher's notes

## Plants for food

### Objectives

- Know that plants form an important part of our diet
- Identify which parts of a plant contain stored energy
- Understand what nutrients a healthy plant requires
- Know that pesticides can build up in the food chain to a dangerous level

### Prior knowledge

Students should know that plants make their own food during photosynthesis (Plants and photosynthesis 9C). Students should also be aware that plant foods form part of a healthy, balanced diet (Fit and healthy 9B, Food and digestion 8A), and that plants are producers, and are always the first link in a food chain.(Environment and feeding relationships 7C).

### QCA link

Unit 9D Plants for food

### NC links

Sc2 Life processes and living things 2k, 3a, 3b, 3c, 3d, 4a, 5a, 5c

### Scottish attainment targets

Environmental studies - Science - living things and the processes of life
Strand - The processes of life
Level E

## Background

Plants use the energy from sunlight to synthesise their food. This food is stored in different parts of the plant. We get essential vitamins and minerals from the plant foods in our diet. Plants also need minerals to keep healthy.

### Starter activity

Ask students to list their favourite fruits and vegetables.

### Activity sheets

'Food from plants'. Ask students to divide a clean piece of paper into four sections. Ask students to label each section as instructed on the activity sheet. Students should then cut out pictures of the different plant foods provided, and stick them in the correct quarter of the page. Encourage students to add more drawings of other foods to each section.

'Where is starch stored in the plant'. Ask students to remember the word equation for photosynthesis. A test for starch is then provided. Ask students to follow the instructions provided to carry out the test. A table has been provided for students to record their results.

'A healthy plant' shows students which minerals are needed by the different parts of a plant. Ask students to use the information provided to draw pictures of four plants which are each deficient in one essential mineral.

'A good growing environment'. Instruct students to divide a clean sheet of paper into three columns. Tell students to label each column using the activity sheet as a guide. Students should then cut out each picture and each word box, and place it in its correct column.

'Pesticides and the food chain sheets 1 and 2' looks at how pesticides are passed up the food chain. Ask a student to read through both activity sheets for the rest of the class. Tell students to use the food chain, which has been provided on sheet 2 as an example, to draw a pyramid to show how pesticides are moved up the food chain. Students should then answer the questions, which follow at the end of both activity sheets. Encourage students to use ICT to find out more about different chemical pollutants and how they can accumulate in the food chain. Direct them to the incidence of mercury poisoning from fish in Japan.

### Plenary

Ask students to design and draw a salad dish that is rich in essential minerals. Encourage them to use unusual fruits, flowers and leaves in their salad.

# Activity sheet – Plants for food

## Food from plants

☞ In your work books, divide one page into four quarters. Label each quarter with one of these words: root, stem, leaf, fruit. Now, cut out each of the 16 boxes below. Stick each fruit and vegetable into its correct place in your work books. Can you think of any more fruits or vegetables, which can be added to each section.

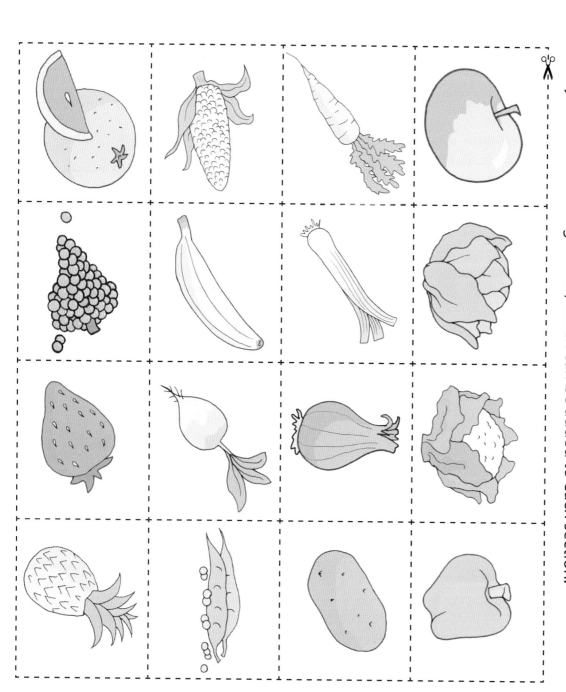

# Where is starch stored in the plant?

☞ Plants make their food using energy from sunlight. Write the equation for photosynthesis in the space provided below.

_____ + _____  ⟹ _____ + _____

using energy from sunlight

The glucose that the plant makes during photosynthesis is changed into starch and stored in different parts of the plant. You can test for starch by adding iodine solution. Iodine solution is brown and it turns black when starch is present.

☞ How to test for starch.

Follow the instructions below to carry out your own experiment to test for starch. Record your results in the table provided.

1.  Put a sample of some plant material onto a white tile and cut it into small pieces. You should use the plant materials in the table below.

2.  Add one or two drops of iodine solution.

3.  Record any colour change in your results table.

| Plant material | Colour change |
| --- | --- |
| Apple | |
| Orange | |
| Potato | |
| Carrot | |
| Bread (wheat) | |
| Cabbage leaf | |
| Celery stalk | |

☞ Now, use your results to answer the following questions.

1.  Which foods turned the iodine solution the blackest?

2.  Which foods contained the most starch?

3.  What do plants use the stored food for?

# A healthy plant

Plants, just like humans need minerals to stay healthy. Plants get these minerals from the soil that they grow in. The diagram below explains how each mineral helps to keep the plant healthy.

**Nitrogen**
Helps make protein for growth and making new cells.

**Phosphorus**
Helps make good, strong roots to help the plant get water and to hold it firmly in the ground.

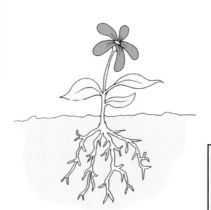

**Potassium**
Helps make flowers for reproduction.

**Magnesium**
Helps make chlorophyll which gives leaves their green colour. Chlorophyll is needed for photosynthesis.

☞ Use the information above to draw four different plants in the boxes provided. Draw each plant without one essential mineral.

Grown without the nutrient nitrogen.

Grown without the nutrient magnesium.

Grown without the nutrient potassium.

Grown without the nutrient phosphorus.

# Activity sheet – Plants for food

# A good growing environment

☞ In your work books, divide a clean sheet of paper into three columns. Label each column **Picture**, **Condition** and **What happens**. Now, cut out each picture and word box provided. Put each one in its correct column in your work books.

| **Picture** | **Condition** | **What happens** |

Ladybirds eat harmful pests like greenfly on the plants.

Space

Plants need energy from sunlight to make their food.

Gentle rainfall adds water to the soil for roots to absorb.

Fertiliser

Rain and water

Replaces the nutrients in the soil that have been used by the growing plants.

Helpful insects

Sunlight

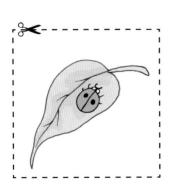

Overcrowding and competition makes plants small and weak.

# Pesticides and the food chain sheet 1

Pesticides are chemicals that kill pests. Farmers spray their fields with chemical pesticides to destroy the weeds in their fields. They do this because the weeds will compete with the farmer's crops for water, sunlight and nutrients in the soil.

In 1939, a pesticide called DDT was used to kill mosquitoes and to control the spread of the disease malaria. Unfortunately, DDT does not break down easily and over time the DDT builds up in the food chain.

This is what happens when DDT is used to spray corn in a field.

## Field food chain

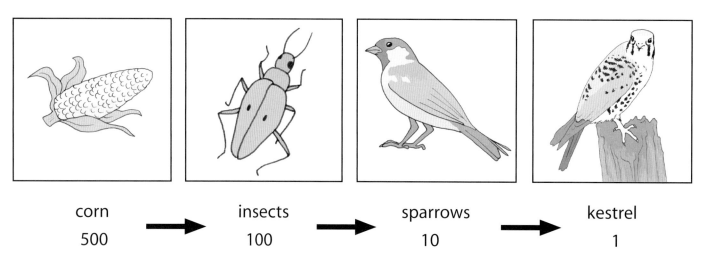

| corn | insects | sparrows | kestrel |
|------|---------|----------|---------|
| 500 | 100 | 10 | 1 |

☞ Draw a pyramid of numbers using the food chain above. Then, turn overleaf.

# Pesticides and the food chain sheet 2

The next food chain shows how the pesticide is passed up the food chain. The DDT is not broken down and stays in corn plants which are eaten by the insects. Each insect eats lots of plant material and, with it, lots of DDT.

The food chain below shows how the DDT moves up the food chain.

## Units of DDT

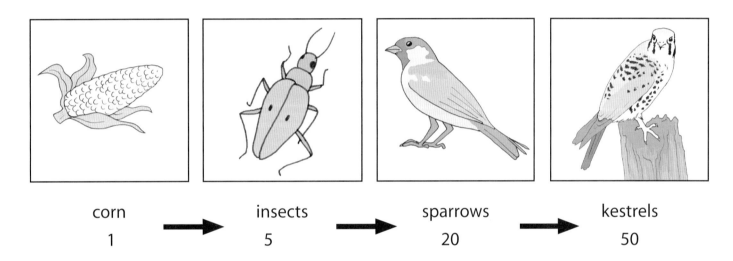

| corn | insects | sparrows | kestrels |
| --- | --- | --- | --- |
| 1 | 5 | 20 | 50 |

☞ Use ICT to help you to answer the following questions. The first answer has been done for you.

1. How does DDT affect birds?
   **Birds sit on their eggs to keep them warm until they hatch. DDT makes the egg shells very thin and weak.**

2. What do you think happened to the eggs of birds affected by DDT?

3. In the 1960s, the population of wild birds like the heron and cormorants fell. Draw a food chain to show how spraying ponds with DDT could affect the heron. **(Clue: herons eat fish.)**

4. At the end of the 1960s, the use of DDT as a pesticide was banned. How do you think this affected the heron population?

## A fair test

### Objectives

- Understand the terms accurate, reliable and fair, as they apply to science
- Be able to select and use the correct apparatus for a given task

### Prior knowledge

Throughout Key Stage 3 students will have handled and used specialist science equipment to carry out a variety of experiments.

### QCA link

*Unit 9M* Investigating scientific questions

### NC links

*Sc1* Scientific enquiry 2d, 2h, 2k, 2m

### Scottish attainment targets

Environmental studies - Science - investigating
Strand - Preparing for tasks
Level D

## Background

Throughout the science syllabus, students will have been encouraged to carry out their own investigations. Much of this topic covers practical and demonstration activities in all three science disciplines. This section allows students to practice specific skills.

### Starter activity

Show students a variety of different chemical glassware and ask them to think of a different experiment, where each piece of equipment is used.

### Activity sheets

'Accurate' explains to students how to measure materials as accurately as possible. Ask students to circle the correct piece of equipment for each task that it might be used for. Using the leftover equipment, ask students to think of a situation where each might be used.

'Accurate measuring instructions' is a practical activity sheet, which follows on from activity sheet, 'Accurate'. Ask students to follow instructions on sheet 1 and write their answers on sheet 2.

'Reliable' teaches students how to obtain the most reliable results possible. Ask students to study the results for an experiment, which are provided. Space has then been allocated for their findings.

'Fair'. Students should answer the questions provided to help them determine how successful an experiment can be.

### Plenary

Ask students to look at some of their own practical activity sheets from previous topics and find examples where they have used a fair test.

# Accurate

Accurate means measuring something as exactly as you can.

☞ Below you will find different pieces of apparatus, which may be used to measure materials for an experiment. Put a circle around the correct apparatus for each experiment provided. Then look at the equipment which is leftover. What might each be used to measure?

1. Which one of these would you use to measure exactly 20ml of copper sulphate solution?

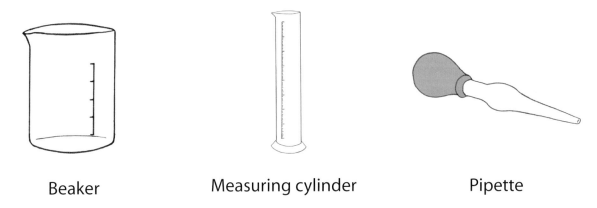

Beaker            Measuring cylinder            Pipette

2. What would you use to measure 5cm of magnesium ribbon?

Ruler            50 metre tape            Thermometer

3. What would you use to measure exactly 25gm of sugar?

Bucket            Bathroom scales            Electronic scales

# Accurate measuring instructions sheet 1

☞ Follow the instructions provided in each box. Once you have done this, turn to the next activity sheet to record your results.

---

**Measuring volume**

1. Half fill a measuring cylinder with water.
2. Pour 25ml of water into the cylinder and then add 15ml more water.
3. Add 100ml of water to the measuring cylinder. Now pour away 20ml of what is left in your measuring cylinder.

---

**Measuring length**

1. Cut a piece of paper exactly 30 cms long.
2. Cut the piece exactly in half.
3. Cut one of the half lengths into three pieces of all the same length.

---

**Weight**

How much does 100ml of water weigh?

1. Weigh an empty beaker.
2. Measure 100ml of water using the measuring cylinder.
3. Pour the water into the beaker and weigh it again.
4. Can you calculate how much only the water weighs?

# Accurate measuring instructions sheet 2

☞ Record your results below.

---

**Measuring volume**

1. The measuring cylinder is half filled with water. It contains _____ml.

2. The total volume of water is _____ml.

3. How much water is left? _____ml.

---

**Measuring length**    Stick your paper here.

Half of the whole 30cm long piece.

The second half length cut into three pieces.

---

**Weight**

Weight of beaker + 100ml of water = _____

Weight of the beaker only          = _____

Weight of 100ml of water          = _____

---

# Reliable

Reliable results are when you get almost the same results every time you repeat your experiment. You should always repeat your experiment to make sure your results are reliable.

☞ Josh and Brenda were both investigating how long it took for 5g of sugar to dissolve in 50ml of warm water. They have recorded their results below.

**Josh's results**

| Experiment | 1 | 2 | 3 | Total | Average time taken |
|---|---|---|---|---|---|
| Time taken (seconds) | 46 | 56 | 57 | 159 | 53 |

**Brenda's results**

| Experiment | 1 | 2 | 3 | Total | Average time taken |
|---|---|---|---|---|---|
| Time taken (seconds) | 57 | 56 | 57 | 170 | 56.6 |

☞ Study both Josh and Brenda's results. Whose results do you think are the most reliable? Why?

_____

_____

_____

# Fair

A **fair** test  is when you only change one thing at a time.

☞ John wanted to see how far a ball would bounce when he dropped it. This is how he carried out his experiment.

1.    For his first experiment he held the ball above his head when he dropped it.

2.    He repeated the experiment but this time he threw the ball up into the air before it bounced on the ground.

3.    For his third attempt John borrowed his friend's ball and threw it against the wall to see how far it would bounce back.

☞ How fair was John's test? Answer these questions.

1.    Was this a fair way to find out how far a ball would bounce when it was dropped?

_____

2.    Make a list of all the things that John changed during his three experiments.

● _____

● _____

● _____

☞ What things would you have kept the same in this experiment?

● _____

● _____

● _____

☞ What one thing would you have changed?

_____

# Teacher's notes

## Collecting data

### Objectives

- Understand why a sample is used
- Be able to use various pieces of equipment to collect data in the field

### Prior knowledge

Students will know some of the food chains, which could be found in the area they are investigating. Students should also know the habitats, where different insects and small animals might be found. (Environment and feeding relationships 7C, Ecological relationships 8D)

### QCA link

*Unit 9M* Investigating scientific questions

### NC links

*Sc1* Scientific enquiry 2a, 2d, 2e, 2f, 2g, 3k, 3m

### Scottish attainment targets

Environmental studies - Science - investigating
Strand - Carrying out tasks
Level D

### Starter activity

Show students different pieces of equipment and ask them what they might be used for.

### Activity sheets

'Collecting data sheets 1 and 2' describe how to use different pieces of equipment to collect data for an ecological study of the school environment. Ask students to study both of the experiments provided. Tell students to study the different pieces of equipment in the examples provided. Ask students to think of something they could use it for. For example, it could be used to find out the most common plant (other than grass) on the school playing field. Alternatively, students could collect some invertebrates, draw them and find out about their preferred habitat. Instruct students to work in groups to make a presentation of their work, to deliver to the rest of the class.

### Plenary

Set aside a whole lesson for the presentations. Presentations could be used for a classroom display.

## Background

This section allows students to get into the field and carry out their own investigations. Students can pose their own questions. For example, *do more daisies grow in the open field, or in the shade under the trees?* Students will be able to collect the right type of data to answer their own questions.

# Collecting data sheet 1

☞ The experiment below can be used for collecting data. Read the experiment carefully. Then answer the questions, which follow. Using the same equipment, can you think of other things you might find out about your school grounds?

**How many daisies?**

Sarah and Aaron wanted to find out about the animals and plants which lived in a field close to their school. They knew that they would not be able to count all the different animals, grass and flowers in the field, so they decided to take a sample. This is what they did.

Sarah and Aaron used a quadrat. A quadrat is a $1m^2$ frame, which they placed randomly over the whole field. They counted the number of daisies in the quadrat each time they used it, and recorded their results. They used a tape measure to find out the size of the field. Then, they calculated the area of the field.

**Sarah and Aaron's results**

| Quadrat No. | 1 | 2 | 3 | 4 | 5 | 6 | 7 | 8 | 9 | 10 | 11 | 12 |
|---|---|---|---|---|---|---|---|---|---|---|---|---|
| No. of daisies | 9 | 7 | 5 | 5 | 3 | 1 | 8 | 9 | 4 | 7 | 7 | 9 |

☞ Sarah and Aaron used the equation below to estimate the population size of daisies in the field. Use the table of Sarah and Aaron's results to complete this equation to find out how many daisies were in the field.

$$\text{Population size} = \frac{\text{Total number of daisies in all quadrats}}{\text{number of quadrats}} \times \text{area of field}$$

# Collecting data sheet 2

**Pitfall traps**

☞ Study the next experiment for collecting data. Answer the questions, which follow.

There are some bigger animals in the field, which Sarah and Aaron also wanted to investigate. To do this, they made some simple pitfall traps to try to catch some invertebrates.

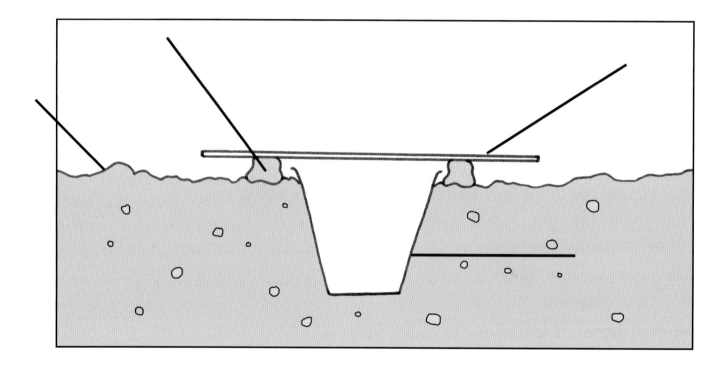

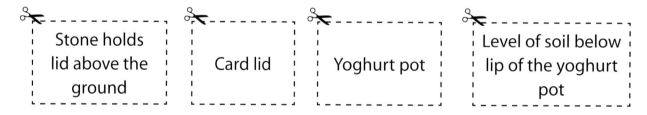

| Stone holds lid above the ground | Card lid | Yoghurt pot | Level of soil below lip of the yoghurt pot |

☞ In your work books, copy the diagram above of Sarah and Aaron's pitfall trap. Cut out the labels provided and use them to label your diagram. Then, write down a few sentences to explain how it works.

# Teacher's notes

## Planning an investigation

### Objectives

- Be able to recognise the possible variables and choose one variable to investigate
- Know how to use scientific knowledge to make a prediction
- Be able to draw an accurate diagram of scientific apparatus
- Know how to plan an experiment, ensuring that it is a fair test

### Prior knowledge

During the course of previous science lessons, students should have already carried out a number of different practical based investigations. Students will also be familiar with the use of writing frames.

### QCA link

Investigating scientific questions 9M

### NC links

Sc1 Scientific enquiry 2a, 2c, 2d, 2e
Sc2 Humans as organisms 2b

### Scottish attainment targets

Environmental studies - Science - investigating
Strand - preparing for tasks
Level D

## Background

This section forms the first part of an investigation booklet designed to encourage students to plan their own scientific investigations. The booklet contains writing frames and prompting questions to guide each student as they carry out the activities. This booklet is based on an investigation of the action of the enzyme trypsin. However, it could easily be adapted for use within other investigations. Use the booklet over three lessons. Include a planning lesson, a practical investigation lesson and a results and evaluation lesson.

### Starter activity

Introduce the trypsin investigation by talking about enzymes and how they work. Explain to students that they will be planning and carrying out their own investigation by themselves.

### Activity sheets

'My science investigation'. Introduce the experiment to the class by discussing enzymes and how they work. Ask students to plan their experiment by answering the questions about what they are going to investigate. A word bank has been provided to help them.

'Planning your experiment' is designed to help students determine how they will carry out this experiment and what apparatus they might use. Have examples of different apparatus on display for students to look at. Then, ask students to make a large labelled diagram of all the apparatus they are going to use. Refer students to the word bank provided, which will help them to think of useful words they might use in their apparatus.

'A fair test'. Ask students to describe how they will carry out a 'fair' test using the prompts. A word bank has been provided to help them.

### Plenary

Tell students to read through their booklet carefully before they carry out the practical activity (which would normally take place during the next lesson).

# My science investigation

☞ Plan your investigation. Use the word bank provided to help you fill in all the gaps.

**What I am going to find out:**

● I am going to find out the best _____ for the enzyme
Trypsin to digest _____ in milk.

● Things that can change are called **variables.** Make a list of things that can change in
this experiment.

I could change:

_____     _____     _____     _____

● **Choose one variable that you are going to investigate.**
I am going to change the _____ of the _____ .

● **What do you think will happen when you change this variable?** (This will be your
prediction. It will say what you expect to happen and why you think this will happen.)

I think that the **_higher/lower_** the temperature of the enzyme Trypsin, the
**_faster/slower_** it will be to break down the protein in milk.

I think this because

_____

_____

> **Word bank**
>
> (You can use all or some of these words. You can also use
> the words more than once.)
>
> protein    temperature    enzyme    volume
> heat    faster    slower    break down

# Planning your experiment

☞ Draw a simple diagram to show how you are going to set up the apparatus for your experiment. Once you have finished, label your diagram. Use the word bank provided to help you.

**Word bank**

(You can use all or some of these words. You can also use the words more than once.)

test tube    beaker    water bath

milk    enzyme    pipette    measuring cylinder

# A fair test

☞ Finish the following sentences. You can use the word bank and the picture provided to help you. You will need to use more than one word in some of the sentences.

1.  To make my test fair I must always use the same amount of _____ and the same amount of _____ .

2.  To measure things accurately I will measure the amount of enzyme and milk using a _____ .

3.  To keep things safe I will _____ .

**Word bank**

(You can use all or some of these words. You can also use the words more than once.)

goggles    test tube    beaker    water bath

milk    enzyme    pipette    measuring cylinder

# Teacher's notes

## Carrying out an investigation booklet

### Objectives

- Use own plans to carry out a practical investigation
- Be able to complete a results table
- Know how to use results to produce a graph
- Be able to formulate a conclusion using own experimental results
- Evaluate the experiment

### Prior knowledge

Students will know how to complete a results table. Students will have also already used experimental results to produce a graph.

### QCA link

*Unit 9M* Investigating scientific questions

### NC links

*Sc1* Scientific enquiry 2f, 2g, 2h, 2i, 2j, 2k, 2l, 2m, 2n, 2p
*Sc2* Humans as organisms 2b

### Scottish attainment targets

Environmental studies - Science- investigating
Strand - Carrying out tasks
Level D

## Background

Students will have already completed the planning part of this investigation booklet and be ready to carry out the experiment. Here, the second half of the booklet will help students to record results and evaluation pages.

### Starter activity

Ask students to read through their plan before they begin the experiment. Tell students to make sure that they have all the equipment they need.

### Activity sheets

'Carrying out the experiment'. Recall the earlier class activities about experimental procedures. Ask students to write down each step for their experiment, in the correct order. Students should use the word bank provided and their own apparatus diagram from 'Planning an investigation booklet' to help them.

'Results and graph hints' is a resource sheet, which students can use when collating their results. Read through the sheet with students before they complete their own results chart and graph, after they have carried out the experiment.

'My experiment'. Students should now carry out their experiments. As they do so, tell students to write down their results in the table provided. Provide students with a sheet of squared paper to draw a graph of their results. Direct students once again to the 'Results and graph hints' resource sheet to help them. Students should then stick their completed graph in the space provided.

'Interpreting.' Ask students to refer to their results to help them fill out this activity sheet. Students should then answer the questions to evaluate their experiment. A word bank has been provided to help them.

### Plenary

Encourage students to look back through their activity booklet. Tell them to complete any sections they may have missed out.

# Carrying out the experiment

☞ Using all the information you recorded in 'Planning your experiment' to help you, write down how you will carry out your experiment.

Write down the amounts (quantities) of things you will be using.

Also, write down any other measurements you will make. You can use the word bank provided to help you. The first step has been done for you.

1. Set up the apparatus as shown in the diagram ('Planning your experiment').

2. _____

_____

_____

3. _____

_____

_____

4. _____

_____

_____

5. _____

_____

_____

6. _____

_____

_____

**Word bank**

(You can use all or some of these words. You can also use some words more than once.)

test tube     stopwatch     pipette     temperature     °C

water bath     milk     stir     clear     Trypsin

# Results chart and graph hints

☞ The information on this sheet will help you to collect and record your results.

### Results chart

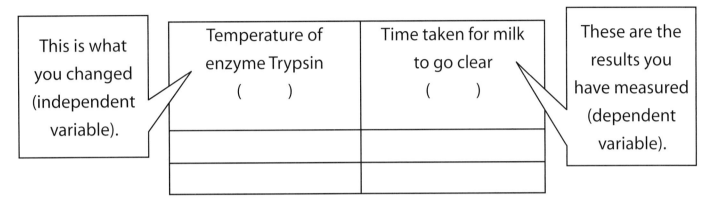

This is what you changed (independent variable).

| Temperature of enzyme Trypsin ( ) | Time taken for milk to go clear ( ) |
|---|---|
|  |  |
|  |  |

These are the results you have measured (dependent variable).

### Graph hints

What to put on your graph.

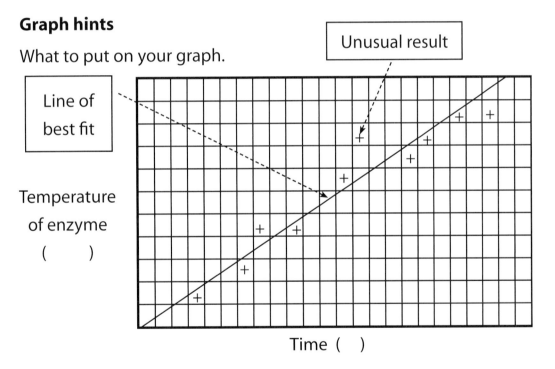

Line of best fit

Unusual result

Temperature of enzyme ( )

Time ( )

☞ Once you have completed your results chart and drawn your graph, you will need to use them to think about the questions below.

1. Are your results reliable?
2. Draw a circle around any unusual (anomalous) results.
3. Draw a line of best fit.

Make sure you:

- write a title;
- put in the units.

# My experiment

☞ Now it is time to carry out your experiment. Record the measurements you have made in the results chart.

**Results chart**

| Temperature of enzyme Trypsin ( ) | Time taken for milk to go clear ( ) |
|---|---|
|  |  |
|  |  |
|  |  |
|  |  |

☞ Now, draw your results graph on a sheet of graph paper. Once you have completed it, cut it out, and stick it in the space below.

**Results graph**

# Interpreting

☞ What conclusions have you drawn (made) from your experiment? Finish the sentences below to show what you have found out. Use the word bank provided to help you.

**Conclusion**

I have found out that as I *increase/decrease* the temperature of the enzyme,

_____ .

My prediction was *right/wrong* because _____

_____

_____ .

My results *do/do not* follow a pattern.

I have put a circle around the results, which are anomalous (do not fit the pattern).

These results do not fit the pattern because _____

_____ .

My experiment *was/was not* a fair test because _____

_____ .

If I could do this experiment again, I would _____

_____ .

**Word bank**

(You can use all or some of these words.

You can also use some words more than once.)

reliable  accurate  graph  milk  clear

pattern  measurements  best fit

# What can I do?

☞ Complete the table below to show what you have learnt.

| What I can do | Example from my work |
|---|---|
| I can use a text to find information. | |
| I can describe my observations using scientific words. | |
| I can record my results in a table. | |
| I can use my own ideas to find the answer to a question. | |
| I can measure quantities accurately. | |
| I can carry out a fair test if I have help. | |
| I can carry out a fair test without help. | |
| I can record my results on a graph. | |
| I can recognise simple patterns in my results. | |
| I can explain simple patterns in my results. | |
| I can make a prediction. | |
| I can suggest improvements for my work. | |